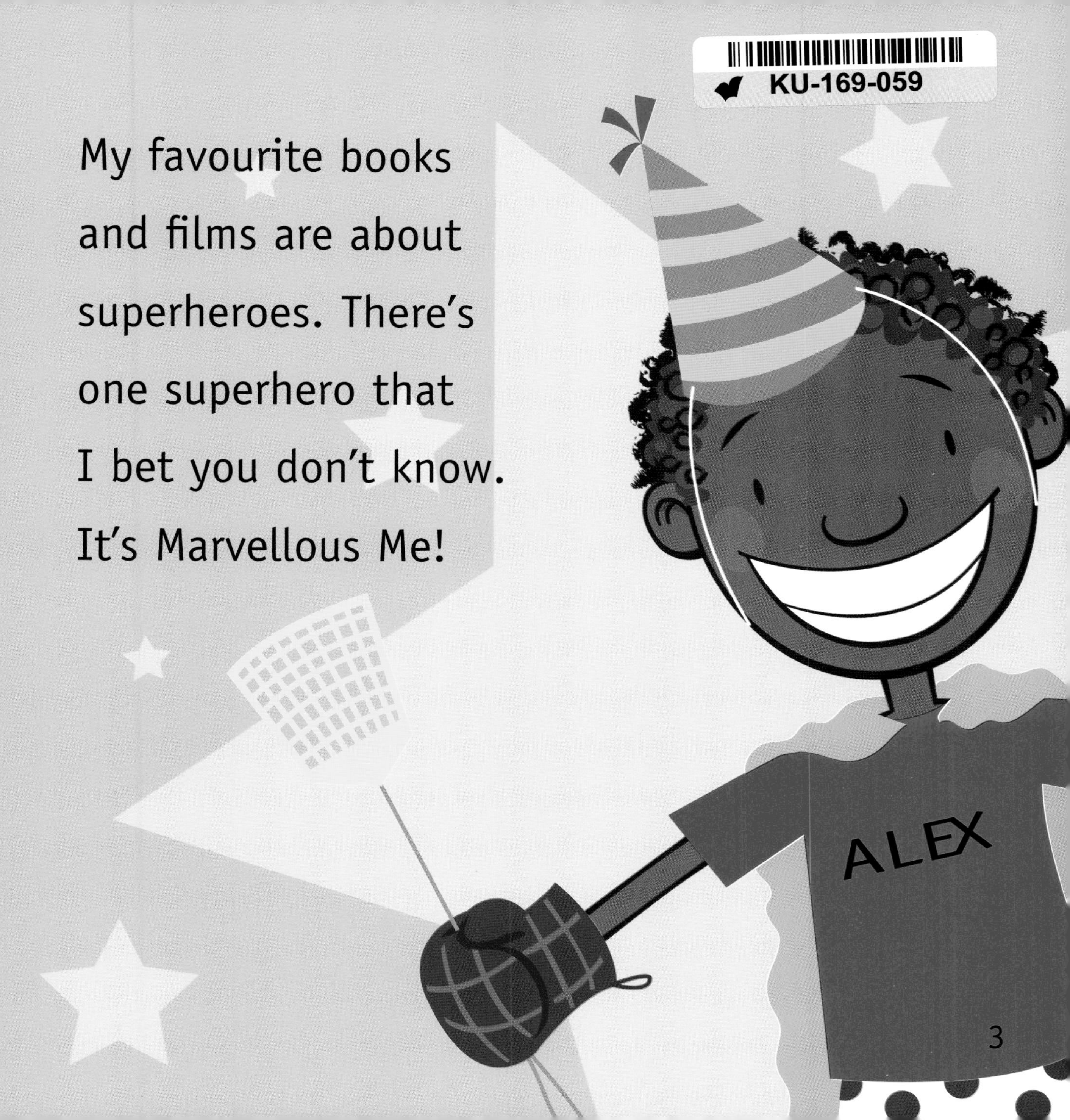

My favourite books and films are about superheroes. There's one superhero that I bet you don't know. It's Marvellous Me!

Marvellous Me can do super-cool things. I have legs that can race a rugby ball. I have eyes that can see far across the pitch. Doing all of these things takes a lot of energy. That's why superheroes have to eat their vegetables.

All About Me

MARVELLOUS ME

Inside and Out

Written by Lisa Bullard • Illustrated by Brandon Reibeling

Raintree is an imprint of Capstone Global Library Limited, a company incorporated in England and Wales having its registered office at 264 Banbury Road, Oxford, OX2 7DY – Registered company number: 6695582

www.raintree.co.uk
myorders@raintree.co.uk

ISBN 978 1 3982 3841 1

Printed and bound in China.

British Library Cataloguing in Publication Data
A full catalogue record for this book is available from the British Library.

My brain can do super things, too.
I can read a comic book all by myself.
I can count all the biscuits in the tin.
I can remember all eight planets and
the name Tyrannosaurus rex.

Marvellous Me can turn the sofa into a pirate's ship and my bike into a racing car. Mum calls that using my imagination. I call it playing make-believe.

Playing pirates and racing car drivers
are only some of my favourite things.
I also love telling knock-knock jokes.
I love polar bears and bats. I can
eat more strawberry ice cream than
any other superhero.

Sometimes superheroes don't feel happy. I felt sad when my best friend, Ramon, moved away. I get cross when my dog chews my toys. I feel bored when I have to clean my room. But Dad says even superheroes have to do their jobs. So when I vacuum, I pretend I'm a roaring dragon.

People get confused sometimes, because there's someone who looks just like me. He's just my size. He's got the same hair and eyes. He's even got the same birthday.

He's my brother, Andy. He's also my twin.

ANDY
ALEX

Andy and I may look the same to you, but our mum and dad know that we're different. Andy likes chocolate ice cream more than strawberry. I'm better at maths, and he's better at reading.

Dad says we each have our own special smile.

ANDY
ALEX

Mum says it's the me inside that makes me special. Nobody else laughs like I do. Nobody else knows how to give my giant bear hug. And only I know all the funny things inside my head.

Inside and out, I'm a super-special superhero. I'm not just Alex, I'm the one and only Marvellous Me!

There's one more superhero I think you already know. Can you guess?

It's Marvellous You!

ALEX

Thinking about being marvellous

Making a Marvellous Me book

Every person is different from every other person. Your favourite things may be completely different from your best friend's. Just how well do you know yourself? How well do your family and friends know you? Try this fun activity.

1. Find three sheets of paper that are all the same size. Holding them together, fold them all in half. Staple several times along the folded edge. You have made a blank book.

2. Think about all of your favourite things. On each page of your book, draw a picture or write down one of your favourite things.

3. Here are some things to ask yourself if you need help filling all the pages:
   What is my favourite colour?
   What is my favourite food?
   What is my favourite animal?
   What is my favourite game?
   What is my favourite film?
   What is my favourite book?

4. Decorate the cover of your book and give it a title. Show your book to some people who think they know you pretty well. Were they surprised by some of your favorite things?

Interviewing another marvellous person

An interview is when one person asks another person lots of questions. You might have seen a reporter interviewing somebody on television, especially on the news or after somebody wins a big sports match. Interviews can be a good way to learn what a person is really like.

1. Get together with a friend or family member. Think of questions to ask each other during the interview and write them down. You can come up with the questions together or make your own lists.

2. Here are some possible questions:
   What's your name?
   How old are you?
   What's your favourite colour?
   What are you good at?
   Do you have any pets?
   What do you like to do for fun?

3. Pretend you are doing an interview for TV, using a hairbrush or a pencil as a microphone. Take turns being the interviewer. Ask all the questions on your list, then let the other person ask you questions. Did you learn something that you didn't know before?

Glossary

energy power that makes something go
imagination the ability to make things up in your mind or think of things you can't actually see
planets large objects in space that move around the sun, such as Earth, Mars and Venus
twins two people or animals who grow at the same time in their mother's body and share a birthday. Some twins, like Alex and Andy, are identical, which means they also look alike.

Find out more

Books

Hey There! What's Your Superpower, Jayneen Sanders (Educate2Empower Publishing, 2019)

Keep Trying! (Mind Matters), Martha E. Rustad (Raintree, 2021)

Websites

BBC Bitesize: Self-esteem
www.bbc.co.uk/programmes/m000xh5q

KidsHealth: Self-esteem
kidshealth.org/en/kids/self-esteem.html